PLOP! No.2s

BY MARTIN BAXENDALE

Published by Silent but Deadly Publications,
4 Catherine's Close, Stroud, Gloucestershire

ISBN 0 9513542 2 1
Printed in Britain by Stoate & Bishop (Printers) Ltd,
Cheltenham & Gloucester

?
EXIT
!
PLOP!

DAY TRIPS
TO THE
SEASIDE
£5 →

At the turd stroke
the time will be
six-turdy precisely...

PLOP!
Come on in... the water's lovely!

Can I interest you in the latest in home insulation?
THERMAL UNDERPANTS CATALOGUE
THERMAL UNDERWEAR

CHANNEL TUNNEL PROJECT
CONTRACTORS: McTURD & CO.
SEWER
PLAN
3017.1
50.2

NAG!
NAG!
NAG!
You're driving me round the bend!

MATERNITY WARD
PUSH!!
PUSH!!

MATERNITY WARD
Stretch marks!
GOO-GOO!
RUB!
RUB!
SKIN CREAM

CHIP!
CHIP!

CHIP!
CHIP!

THE STINKER

....so what does the turd in the street think?
T.T.V.

FARP!
31
WIND-
SURFING
CLUB

They'd grow much better if you dug some manure into the soil...

FART!
SNIFF!
SNIFF!
Must you keep making those revolting smells?!

I can do sir a nice double-breasted suit with waistcoat and matching sports-jacket
LIGHTWEIGHT NATURAL FIBRE

BOING!
Bloody show-off!
PLOP!

I'm taking the dogshit for a walk... he hasn't been out all day

POT-HOLING
CLUB

PONY-DROPPINGS CLUB
ANNUAL GYMKHANA
.... and it's a clear round for Charlotte Effluent-Wasteproduct on "Plop-plop Excrement The Third"....
SPLUDGE!
GALLOP!
NEIGH!
SPLUDGE!

PLOP!

Come on out, Malone! We know you're in there!
FEDERAL POLICE

BROWNIES
SUMMER
CAMP

MINISTRY OF DEFENCE
CHEMICAL WARFARE LAB.
RESTRICTED AREA
Our latest secret weapon, General...
CHEMICAL TOILET
Mk. I

Hello my little honey-bun, my little sugar-pie lovey-dovey... kissie, kissie!
Oh god! Must you be so bloody sloppy?

Nice head of worms you have there, sir! Which side do you want the parting?
SHAM-POO
HAIR SPRA

BRRRRATATATATAT!
Curse you, Brown Baron!
VVRROOOM!

Bloody dogshit!

SALE OF
CUDDLY TOYS
ALL PRICES REDUCED
CUDDLY RABBIT DROPPINGS
CUDDLY PUPPY POOH
CUDDLY PONY DROPPINGS
CUDDLY ELEPHANT DROPPINGS

SPLURP!
SPORT
DIP!
DIP!
HP
SPORT
CHOMP!
MUNCH!
DIP!
DIP!
!
MUNCH!
CHOMP!
SPORT

Mmmm... I just **love** sausages!
SPORT
MUSTA